Book br

1 1908 novel by Canadian writer Lucy Maud Montgomery, written for all ages and considered a classic children's novel since the mid-20th century.

2 Set in the late 19th century, it tells the story of the adventures of Anne Shirley, an 11-year-old orphan sent by mistake to live with Matthew and Marilla Cuthbert who originally wanted a boy to help on their farm.

3 The book follows the formula of orphan stories that were popular at that time.

4 Translated into at least 36 languages, it's one of the best-selling books worldwide, with more than 50 million copies sold.

5 There are several film versions, musicals, cartoons and TV series based on the book, as well as plays with annual productions in Europe and Japan.

In this reader:

 21st Century Skills — To encourage students to connect the story to the world they live in.

 Movers — A1 level activities.

Story Notes — A brief summary of the text.

Glossary — Explanation of difficult words.

Picture Caption — A brief explanation of the picture.

Audio — These icons indicate the parts of the story that are recorded.
- ▶ start
- ■ stop

Think — To encourage students to develop their critical thinking skills.

Lucy Maud Montgomery

Anne of Green Gables

Retold and Activities by
Michael Lacey Freeman

Illustrated by
Gaia Bordicchia

Teen ELi Readers

Teen Eli Readers

The **ELI Readers** collection is a complete range of books and plays for readers of all ages, ranging from captivating contemporary stories to timeless classics. There are four series, each catering for a different age group: **First ELI Readers, Young ELI Readers, Teen ELI Readers** and **Young Adult ELI Readers**. The books are carefully edited and beautifully illustrated to capture the essence of the stories and plots. The readers are supplemented with 'Focus on' texts packed with background cultural information about the writers and their lives and times.

Anne of Green Gables
By Lucy Maud Montgomery
Retold and Activities by
Michael Lacey Freeman
Language Level Consultant
**Janet Borsbey, Ruth Swan
and Silvana Sardi**
Illustrated by **Gaia Bordicchia**

ELI Readers
Founder and Series Editors
**Paola Accattoli, Grazia Ancillani,
Daniele Garbuglia (Art Director)**

Graphic Design
**Andersen
the Premedia Company**

Production Manager
Francesco Capitano

Photo credits
Shutterstock

New edition: **2021**
First edition: **2013**

© **ELI s.r.l.**
**P.O. Box 6
62019 Recanati (MC)
Italy
T +39 071750701
F +39 071977851
info@elionline.com
www.elionline.com**

Typeset in 12 / 17 pt
Fulmar designed by Leo Philp

Printed in Italy by
**Tecnostampa - Pigini Group
Printing Division
Loreto - Trevi (Italia) -
ERT 110.10
ISBN 978-88-536-3184-8**

Contents

Matthew
*Marilla's brother - he's a kind,
quiet man who likes Anne
from the moment he sees her.*

Marilla
*Matthew's sister - at first she
doesn't want Anne to stay
then she learns to love her.*

Anne
*11 years old and with no mother or father.
She loves talking about her dreams and
she doesn't like her red hair.*

Rachel
She lives near Matthew and Marilla and always wants to know everything about everybody.

Diana
She's the same age as Anne and lives near Green Gables. She's Anne's best friend.

Gilbert
2 years older than Anne - he's smart and good-looking.

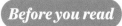

Grammar

1 **Read this dialogue and complete the questions and answers with *did* or *didn't*.**

'When ____did____ Lucy Maud Montgomery write *Anne of Green Gables*?' 'In 1908.'

1 'How _____ people travel at that time?'

2 'People _____ travel by car. They often walked.'

3 '_____ people have telephones?'

4 'No, they _____ .'

5 'Where _____ people buy food?'

6 'They _____ go to supermarkets. They went to small shops.'

7 'What _____ people do in their free time?'
'They visited their friends for tea.'

2 **Complete the sentences with *is, are, do* or *does*.**

| is   doesn't   ~~are~~   is   aren't   doesn't   haven't   is |

Matthew and Marilla Cuthbert ____are____ brother and sister.
They live in a town called Avonlea, which (**1**) _____ in Canada.
They live and work on their farm. They (**2**) _____ married and
(**3**) _____ got any children. They want someone to help
on their farm.

Rachel Lynde (**4**) _____ a friend of Matthew and Marilla's.
She also lives in Avonlea. She (**5**) _____ know that Matthew and
Marilla are looking for a boy to help on their farm.

Anne (**6**) _____ eleven years old. She comes to live with
Matthew and Marilla. She (**7**) _____ know that Matthew and
Marilla want a boy and not a girl.

Vocabulary

3 **Match the adjectives that mean the opposite.**

1 ☐ bad		**a** last
2 ☐ big		**b** late
3 ☐ early		**c** little
4 ☐ first		**d** good
5 ☐ happy		**e** strange
6 e normal		**f** unhappy

Reading and Writing MOVERS

4 **Look at the pictures and choose the correct word for each definition.**

farmer   station   freckles   pond

smile   countryside   dinner   mirror

    There's lots of green in this place.   *countryside*

1 There's water in this place.   _____

2 Anne has some of these on her face.   _____

3 You go here to catch a train.   _____

4 You can see yourself if you look in this.   _____

5 This person works outside.   _____

Writing

5 **Complete this table.**

 21st Century Skills

year		1908	Now (1)
travel		(2)	(3)
telephone		no	(4)
Buy food		(5)	(6)
Free time		(7)	(8)

9

Chapter 1

Anne Arrives[1] at Green Gables

2 Matthew Cuthbert lived with his sister, Marilla. The name of their house was Green Gables. It was in a little town called Avonlea. Matthew was a farmer. He worked hard on his farm every day.

One afternoon, Matthew went out in his buggy[2]. He had to do something important. His friend, Rachel Lynde, was very surprised to see him go out.

'That's strange,' she said. 'Matthew never goes out.'

Rachel went to speak to Marilla about this.

When Rachel arrived at Green Gables, she asked Marilla, 'Where's Matthew going?'

'He's going to Bright River Station,' said Marilla. He's meeting a little boy. The boy doesn't have a mother or a father. He's an orphan[3]. We want the orphan boy to live with us. Our friend, Mrs. Spencer, helped us to find him. Matthew is 60 years old now and he needs some help on the farm.'

Rachel wasn't happy to hear this. *Why didn't they tell me about this before,* she thought. *It's a bad*

---

[1] **to arrive** to come to
[2] **buggy** a type of transport. You need a horse. See the picture on page 13
[3] **orphan** a child with no mother or father

idea to invite a stranger to their house.

Matthew enjoyed his journey[1] to Bright River Station. It was a beautiful road with lots of apple trees. When he arrived, he didn't see a boy at the station. There was just a girl. There was a man there. The man said, 'That little girl is waiting for you. She's from the orphanage[2].'

'But that's not possible!' said Matthew. 'I have to meet a little boy, not a girl.'

Matthew didn't like speaking to people, but he had to speak to the little girl. He didn't speak first because the little girl spoke first. Her name was Anne Shirley. She had lots of red hair and lots of freckles[3] on her face. She was very happy to see Matthew. She talked a lot. 'Are you Matthew of Green Gables?' she asked. 'I'm so happy to meet you. My name's Anne Shirley. But you can call me Anne.'

At first, Matthew didn't know what to do. Then he decided[4] to take Anne home. *Marilla can decide what to do*, thought Matthew.

On the way home, Anne chatted[5] all the time.

Matthew goes to the station to get a boy from the orphanage, but when he gets there, Anne is waiting for him. He and his sister wanted a boy to help them on their farm. Matthew doesn't know what to do so he takes Anne home to Green Gables.

[1] **journey** you go on a journey when you travel from one place to another place
[2] **orphanage** a place for children who have no mother or father
[3] **freckles** Anne has some of these on her face. They are brown spots on your face and body
[4] **to decide** when you think about doing something and then you do it
[5] **to chat** to talk

'I don't like my red hair and freckles. I want to have black hair, but it's red and I can't change the colour.'

Anne enjoyed the journey. She thought the countryside was very beautiful. She saw a road called *The Avenue*. Anne had a lot of imagination[1]. She called it, 'The White Way of Delight[2].' Then she saw a pond[3]. It was just a normal[4] pond, but Anne used her imagination again. She called it 'The Lake of Shining Waters[5].'

Matthew was silent. He enjoyed listening to Anne. He didn't have to say anything because Anne talked all the time.

When they were very near Green Gables, Anne saw a house and said, 'That's it! That's Green Gables.' She was right.

They arrived at Green Gables and Marilla opened the door. When she saw Anne, she said, 'Where's the boy? There must be a boy! We asked for a boy!'

Anne listened in silence. Then she cried, 'You don't want me because I'm not a boy. Nobody wants me!'

Marilla is very surprised when she sees Anne. She wanted a boy not a girl.

Anne is going with Matthew to Green Gables and she sees the pond that she calls "The Lake of Shining Waters".

[1] **imagination** things you think of that are different from what you really see
[2] **delight** something that makes you very happy
[3] **pond** a small lake
[4] **normal** something is normal when you usually hear or see it
[5] **shining waters** water that has many different colours

Marilla and Matthew didn't know what to do. They decided to wait until the morning. It was late. They couldn't do anything today.

They had dinner, but Anne couldn't eat. She was very sad. Anne went to bed. Anne's bedroom was very empty[1]. There was only a bed, a small table and a little mirror. Near the table, there was a window.

Later, Marilla spoke to Matthew about Anne. 'We have to send her back to the orphanage. I want to take her to Mrs. Spencer's house tomorrow.'

Matthew didn't agree[2].

'Why?' asked Marilla. 'How can she be good for us?'

'We can be good for her,' replied[3] Matthew.

Early in the morning, Anne woke up. At first, she didn't remember anything. *Where am I?* she thought. Then she remembered. This was Green Gables and they didn't want her here. She wasn't a boy! Anne opened the bedroom window. It was a beautiful morning. There was a lovely garden and lots of trees, but Anne had to leave. Just then, Marilla came in, 'We have to go soon,' she said.

After breakfast, Anne and Marilla went to

Matthew wants Anne to stay but his sister Marilla wants to send her back to the orphanage.

[1] **empty** with nothing in it
[2] **to agree** when you think what another person says is right
[3] **to reply** you do this when you answer a question

Mrs. Spencer's house. They went in the buggy. Anne was very unhappy, but she wanted to enjoy the journey. Anne chatted a lot and Marilla said, 'You enjoy talking. So, … talk to me about your life.'

So Anne told Marilla her story.

'I was eleven years old in March. I was born in Bolingbroke in Nova Scotia. My mother and father died when I was only three months old. Then I lived with different families. One day, I had to go to the orphanage. I was at the orphanage for four months, and now I'm here with you.'

Marilla listened to Anne's sad story. For the first time, she thought, *Maybe I'm wrong. Can she stay with us?*

Soon they arrived at Mrs. Spencer's big yellow house. Mrs. Spencer apologised[1] to Marilla, 'I'm sorry, I didn't know you wanted a boy, and not a girl.'

'Can Anne go back to the orphanage?' asked Marilla.

'Yes,' said Mrs. Spencer, 'but Mrs. Blewett is looking for a little girl. Anne can live with her.'

Marilla didn't like this idea. She knew that Mrs. Blewett was unkind[2] to children. Then, Mrs. Blewett arrived. 'Mrs. Blewett, do you want

[1] **to apologise** to say that you're sorry
[2] **unkind** not nice

to take this little girl home with you?' said Mrs. Spencer. Mrs. Blewett looked at Anne. Anne was frightened of her.

'How old are you and what's your name?' asked Mrs. Blewett.

When Marilla hears Anne's sad story and also that Mrs. Blewett, an unkind woman, wants Anne, she decides to take Anne back to Green Gables to live with her and Matthew.

'My name ... My name's Anne and I'm ... I'm eleven years old,' said Anne.

'Well, I can take her home now,' said Mrs. Blewett.

'I don't know,' said Marilla, 'I want to take her home again. I need to talk to Matthew about this.'

Then there was a big smile on Anne's face.

'Oh Miss Cuthbert, can I stay?' said Anne.

'We have to decide,' said Marilla.

Anne and Marilla returned[1] to Green Gables. Marilla didn't say anything to Matthew at first. When they were alone[2], Marilla told Matthew, 'Anne can stay. We can tell her tomorrow.'

Matthew was very happy. That evening Marilla told Anne to say a prayer[3]. In her bedroom Anne said the prayer. Marilla listened to her. Anne thanked God for the 'White Way of Delight', and the 'Lake of Shining Waters'. And then she said, 'Please can I stay at Green Gables?'

Anne is saying a prayer in her bedroom and Marilla is listening to her. Anne wants to stay at Green Gables.

> **Think**
> Marilla and Matthew are much older than Anne. Do you think the girl can be happy with them?

[1] **to return** to go back
[2] **alone** (here) only the two of them
[3] **prayer** when you talk to God, you say a prayer

Reading and Writing MOVERS

21st Century Skills

1 Look at this picture again.
Complete the sentences and answer the questions.

The people are in a _____*buggy*_____ .

1 Who's sitting next to Anne? _____

2 Anne has long red _____ .

3 How many trees are there in the picture? _____

4 What's Anne looking at? _____

Speaking and Writing

21st Century Skills

2 A **Complete this table about you and Anne.**
Are any of your answers the same?

	Anne	You
Nationality	Canadian	(1)
Age	(2)	(3)
Freckles	yes	(4)
Birthday in	(5)	(6)
Family	None	(7)

2 B **Discuss these questions with a partner and write your answers.**

1 Anne doesn't like the colour of her hair.
Do you like yours?

2 Anne thought the countryside was beautiful.
What do you like more, the countryside
or a big city? Why?

3 Anne's bedroom was very empty.
What's your bedroom like?

4 Anne talks a lot. Do you talk a lot or do you listen more?

Grammar

3 **Complete the questions and then complete the answers.**

| What | Where | Who | Why |

_____*Who*_____ does Rachel see in his buggy?
*She sees Matthew.*_____

1 _____ does Matthew go?
_____ to the station.

2 _____ does Matthew meet at the station?
_____ Anne.

3 _____ does Anne call the Pond?
_____ The Lake of Shining Waters.

4 _____ does Anne cry?
_____ because Matthew and
Marilla want a boy and not a girl.

5 _____ do Anne and Marilla go in the morning?
_____ to Mrs. Spencer's house.

6 _____ does Anne want when she says her prayer?
_____ to stay at Green Gables.

Before-reading Activity

Listening

▶ 3 **4** **Look at these statements. Tick (✓) the ones that you think are true in Chapter 2. Listen and check.**

Anne can stay at Green Gables. (✓) Anne can't stay at
Green Gables. ( )

1 Anne can call Marilla 'aunt'. ( ) Anne can't call Marilla 'aunt'. ( )

2 Anne meets a little girl. ( ) Anne doesn't meet a little girl. ( )

3 Marilla likes listening to Anne. ( ) Marilla doesn't like
listening to Anne. ( )

4 Anne is angry with Rachel. ( ) Anne isn't angry with Rachel. ( )

Chapter 2

Anne Finds a Friend

▶ 3 In the afternoon, Marilla spoke to Anne. 'You can stay at Green Gables,' said Marilla. Anne was very happy.

'Can I call you 'aunt'?' asked Anne.

'No, because I'm not really your aunt,' said Marilla.

'But can you imagine[1] that you're my aunt?'

'No, I can't,' said Marilla. 'I don't like imagining things.'

'Oh Marilla, it's so sad not to have an imagination.'

Then Marilla told Anne some more good news[2]. 'There's a young girl, Diana. She lives near Green Gables. One day, you can meet her. Maybe[3] you can be friends.'

A real friend, thought Anne. Anne wanted a friend very much. She went to her bedroom and looked in the mirror and said, 'You're only Anne of Green Gables, but it's good to be Anne of Green Gables!'

Marilla tells Anne she can stay at Green Gables and the girl is very happy.

---

[1] **to imagine** to think something is real when it isn't
[2] **news** new information
[3] **maybe** it's possible

For the next two weeks, Anne helped Marilla in the house. She went for a walk every day. She looked at every tree in the area. She visited every pond and every lake. Matthew loved listening to Anne. Marilla also enjoyed listening to Anne. But she didn't tell Anne this.

One morning, Rachel Lynde arrived. She wanted to see Anne. When Rachel arrived, she asked Marilla, 'Why didn't Anne go back to the orphanage?'

'We quite like her,' said Marilla. 'Of course, she has to learn many things. Everything is new for her. We need to teach her these things.'

At that moment, Anne ran into the house.

'Well,' said Rachel. 'You look very skinny[1] and plain[2] ... and with your red hair ... well, you look like a carrot.'

'I HATE[3] YOU!' cried[4] Anne. You're a very rude[5] woman!' (■)

Rachel Lynde comes to see Anne and she's rude to her. She makes Anne very angry and the girl shouts at her.

(▶)4 Anne went to her bedroom. Marilla was angry

---

[1] **skinny** very thin
[2] **plain** ordinary, nothing special
[3] **to hate** to really not like
[4] **to cry (here)** to say something in a loud voice, often when you're angry
[5] **rude** not kind

with Anne. It was rude to speak to an adult[1] in that way. Marilla was also angry with Rachel. 'You were very unkind to Anne,' said Marilla to Rachel.

'Don't forget, Anne doesn't know what's right, and what's wrong. She needs to learn.'

Rachel was also angry and she went home. Now Marilla had to make a decision[2]. She had to punish[3] Anne.

Soon, she decided what to do. She went to Anne's bedroom and said, 'Anne, you must apologise to Rachel.'

'I can never apologise to that rude woman,' said Anne.

'Then you must stay in your room,' said Marilla.

The next day, breakfast, lunch and dinner passed. Anne wasn't there. It was very quiet at the table. Anne ate in her room. She didn't eat very much.

That evening, Marilla went out. Matthew went to Anne's room. Anne smiled when she saw Matthew. But she was very sad.

'Anne,' said Matthew. 'It's better to say sorry to Rachel. You must say sorry one day. Why not say sorry now?'

Rachel Lynde is very rude to Anne. Anne is angry with Rachel and shouts at her.

---

[1] **adult** when you're over 18 years of age you're an adult
[2] **to make a decision** to choose what to do
[3] **to punish** Marilla does this. She tells Anne to do something, because Anne was rude to Rachel.

'Alright, only for you, to make you happy,' said Anne.

The next day, Anne and Marilla went to Rachel's house to apologise. When they arrived, Anne said to Rachel, 'I'm so sorry, Mrs. Rachel. I also want to say sorry to Marilla and Matthew. They're so kind to me. Thanks to them, I can stay at Green Gables. Please forgive[1] me!'

At first Anne doesn't want to apologise to Rachel for shouting at her, then she decides to say sorry to make Matthew happy.

Rachel was happy that Anne said she was sorry. 'Maybe I was wrong to speak to you in that way, and maybe, in the future, the colour of your hair will be better.'

On the way home, Anne chatted to Marilla. Marilla had a strange feeling. Maybe it was love, for this little girl.

One day, Anne went to Sunday School[2]. Marilla made a dress for her. Anne didn't like it. It was dark and plain. On the way to Sunday School, she saw some flowers. She put them on her hat. At the school, there were some girls. They had beautiful pink and blue dresses. The girls looked at Anne. She was strange, with her plain dress and flowers in her hat.

❯

Anne is at Sunday Scho but she isn't very happy because the other girls think she looks strang with her plai dark dress a flowers in he hat.

[1] **to forgive** if you forgive someone you're not angry with them anymore for something bad they did to you in the past
[2] **Sunday School** a school to learn about religion

When Anne came home, she spoke to Marilla about Sunday School.

'I didn't like Sunday School very much,' said Anne to Marilla. 'I don't think it's very interesting¹. I answered all the teacher's questions. But I often looked out of the window. I could see the Lake of Shining Waters.'

'You must think more about your lessons,' said Marilla.

On Friday, Anne and Marilla went to Diana's house. Anne was excited but also worried. *I hope that Diana likes me*, she thought.

They arrived at Diana's house. Diana was beautiful. She had dark hair and black eyes. She had a happy expression².

'This is Anne,' said Marilla. 'Diana, take Anne to the garden to look at the flowers.' Anne and Diana went into the garden.

'Oh, Diana,' said Anne, 'do you think we can be best friends forever?'

'I think so,' said Diana. 'It'll be nice to have a friend to play with.'

Anne and Diana promised³ to be best friends.

Anne doesn't like Sunday School because the lessons aren't interesting and the other girls think she's strange.

¹ **interesting** if something is interesting you like doing it or reading about it
² **expression** the expression on your face tells others what you're thinking or feeling
³ **to promise** to agree to do something always

They made a special promise. They looked at each other and said, 'I'll be your special friend forever.'

Diana thought that Anne was very strange. But she was very happy to have this new friend. Anne was different from other girls. 'You're a strange girl, Anne, but I like you,' she said.

Anne was very happy. Finally[1], she had a real friend, not an imaginary friend, but a real friend.

Later, Matthew came home. He gave Anne a box of sweets. Anne was so happy. *I can give some of the sweets to Diana*, she thought.

On Sunday, Anne had some exciting news for Marilla.

'Oh, Marilla,' she said, 'there's a Sunday School picnic next week with real ice cream. Just imagine, real ice cream! Can I go? Please can I go?'

Marilla agreed. 'You can go to the picnic,' she said.

'But,' said Anne, 'everybody must take a picnic basket[2] of things to eat. How can I go without one?'

'Don't worry, I can make some food for you,' said Marilla.

So, for the rest of the week, Anne was very excited. She talked about the picnic. She thought about the picnic. And she dreamed about the picnic. ⬤

Anne is happy because she has a new friend, Diana, and also because she can go on the picnic.

Think
Where do you think the best place is to have a picnic?

[1] **finally** in the end
[2] **basket** you put things in a basket, like fruit and food

Reading

1 **Read these sentences and tick (✓) the ones that are true.**

    Anne hears that she can stay at Green Gables.   (✓)

1 Anne doesn't have time to play outside.   ( )
2 Marilla doesn't like listening to Anne.   ( )
3 Rachel says that Anne is very skinny.   ( )
4 Anne says sorry to Rachel.   ( )
5 Anne likes her Sunday School dress.   ( )
6 Anne doesn't think that Sunday School is very interesting. ( )
7 Anne meets Diana at Green Gables.   ( )
8 Anne eats all the sweets that Matthew gives her.   ( )
9 Marilla agrees to make some food for the picnic.   ( )

Reading and Writing MOVERS

2 **These words are all in Chapter 2. Look at the pictures and choose the correct word for each definition.**

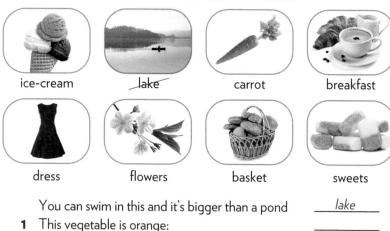

ice-cream	lake	carrot	breakfast
dress	flowers	basket	sweets

    You can swim in this and it's bigger than a pond   _lake_

1 This vegetable is orange: _____
2 These can be bad for your teeth: _____
3 You can see these in the garden: _____
4 You can put food in this for a picnic: _____
5 This is cold and yummy: _____

Speaking

③ Talk to a partner about these questions. How many of your answers are the same?

1 Anne tells Marilla it's sad that she doesn't have an imagination. When do you use your imagination?

2 Anne helps Marilla in the house. Tick the things that you do to help at home.

 ☐ wash the dishes

 ☐ dust the furniture

 ☐ make the bed

 ☐ cook

 ☐ throw the rubbish away

 ☐ clean the windows

3 Anne is angry with Rachel Lynde because she's rude to her. What makes you angry?

4 Do you think Anne was right to apologise to Rachel? Why / Why not?

5 Anne is happy to have Diana as her best friend. Do you think it's a good idea to have one best friend or lots of friends?

Before-reading Activity

Listening

④ In the next chapter there are 3 new characters. Listen and complete the sentences.

▶ 6　1 Mr. Phillips - Mr. Phillips, the teacher, was __strange__ . He was (1) _____ and skinny. He didn't listen to Anne. Another student called Prissy Andrews was his favourite student.

▶ 7　2 Gilbert Blythe - Diana talked about a boy called Gilbert Blythe. Gilbert was in their class. Everybody at school liked him. He had (2) _____ hair and green (3) _____ .

▶ 9　3 Mrs. Barry - Marilla and Anne tried to explain everything to Diana's mother, Mrs. Barry. Mrs. Barry was (4) _____ with black hair and (5) _____ eyes, like Diana.

Chapter 3

Anne Starts School

▶5 One day, Anne and Marilla were at home. 'Where's my brooch¹? I can't find it.' said Marilla.

'I played with it in your bedroom,' said Anne. 'But only in your bedroom.'

But Marilla couldn't find the brooch in her room. 'Did you lose it?' asked Marilla.

'No, I didn't lose it,' replied Anne.

Marilla didn't believe² her.

'I didn't do anything,' said Anne.

'Well, you aren't going to the picnic on Wednesday afternoon,' said Marilla.

Wednesday morning arrived. It was the day of the picnic. Anne decided to apologise to Marilla. She really wanted to go to the picnic. 'I took the brooch!' said Anne to Marilla. 'I played with it near the Lake of Shining Waters. I lost it there.'

Anne asked for her punishment. She wanted her punishment before the picnic. But the punishment was... that she couldn't go to the picnic.

Marilla can't find her brooch. Anne didn't take it but she says she lost it so that she can do her punishment before the picnic. Marilla says her punishment is that she can't go on the picnic!

¹ **brooch** a piece of jewellery you usually put on a jacket or jumper
² **to believe** if you believe someone you think what they say is true.

Anne was very unhappy. At lunch she didn't eat anything. After lunch there was a great surprise. Marilla found the brooch. It was on her old dress! Anne's story about the brooch wasn't true.

'I'm sorry that I didn't believe you,' said Marilla. 'But I'm also angry about your story. You didn't lose the brooch at the Lake of Shining Waters. Listen, I'll say I'm sorry if you say you're sorry.'

Marilla and Anne apologised. 'You can go on the picnic now, Anne.' said Marilla.

So Anne went to the picnic. She enjoyed it very much.

When she returned from the picnic, she was very happy, and very tired.

'Oh Marilla, the picnic was wonderful[1]. We had tea and then we went on a boat on the Lake of Shining Waters. The ice cream was delicious[2]. I can't describe[3] that ice cream in words.' Anne was happy again.

On the first day of September, Anne started school. She enjoyed her first day. ◼

6   Mr. Phillips, the teacher, was strange. He was tall and skinny. He didn't listen to Anne. Another

Marilla finds her brooch so Anne can go on the picnic and she loves it.

---

[1] **wonderful** very good
[2] **delicious** we say this about food that is very good
[3] **to describe** to talk about something

student called Prissy Andrews was his favourite student, but Anne was happy because she sat next to her best friend, Diana. ▣

▶7 Three weeks later, Anne and Diana walked to school. The road to school was beautiful. Diana talked about a boy called Gilbert Blythe. Gilbert was in their class. Everybody at school liked him. He had brown hair and green eyes. ▣

▶8 At school, Anne didn't look at Gilbert. She looked at the Lake of Shining Waters. Gilbert wanted Anne to look at him. So later that day, he did something very bad. He laughed at[1] Anne's hair and shouted:

'Carrots, Carrots!'

'You horrible[2] boy!' shouted Anne and she hit Gilbert on the head with her book.

Mr. Phillips decided to punish Anne, and not Gilbert. Anne had to stand in front of the blackboard[3] all afternoon.

'I was wrong, not Anne,' said Gilbert. 'You must punish me and not Anne.' But Mr. Phillips only

At school, Anne hits Gilbert Blythe because he laughs at her hair.
Mr. Phillips the teacher, punishes her, not Gilbert even if the boy says he was wrong and not Anne.

❯

Anne is hitt
Gilbert on t
head with h
book becau
he laughed
at her hair
and called h
'Carrots'.

[1] **to laugh at (someone/something)** to laugh in a negative way
[2] **horrible** not nice
[3] **blackboard** the place where the teacher writes in front of the class

Gilbert apologises to Anne but she doesn't want to talk to him. Then the teacher only punishes Anne when she and 12 other students arrive late for school, so Anne decides she doesn't want to go to school anymore.

punished Anne. Mr. Phillips wrote something on the blackboard:

Anne Shirley has a very bad temper[1]. Anne Shirley must learn to control her bad temper.

Anne decided never to look at Gilbert again. Gilbert apologised a lot, but Anne didn't say anything, but that wasn't the end of Anne's problems. One day Anne arrived late for school. Twelve of Anne's classmates[2] also arrived late for school, but Mr. Phillips didn't punish the other students. He only punished Anne and her punishment was ... to sit next to Gilbert Blythe!

Gilbert wanted to give Anne some sweets, but Anne didn't want to talk to Gilbert.

On that day, Anne made an important decision. 'I'll never go to school again!' said Anne.

At home, Anne told Marilla about her decision. Marilla didn't know what to do. Then Marilla decided to ask Rachel for some advice[3]. 'Don't do anything. Don't say anything,' said Rachel. 'I'm sure after a few days she'll return to school.'

Marilla agreed with Rachel. She decided not to say anything to Anne. Anne was sad because

---

[1] **bad temper** someone with a bad temper gets angry very quickly
[2] **classmates** students, just like Anne
[3] **advice** what someone tells you to do to help you with a problem

she didn't see Diana at school, but she played with Diana after school. 'I like playing with Diana so much,' she told Marilla. 'I hope[1] Diana never leaves me.'

When Anne said this, Marilla laughed so much. Matthew was surprised. It was strange to hear Marilla laugh like that.

Soon, it was October. She enjoyed the beautiful colours of autumn. 'I'm so happy to live in a world where there are Octobers,' she said. 'I don't want to live in a world where, after September, it's November.' Anne was happy, but soon, there were more problems.

One day, Marilla had to go out. 'Anne, you can invite Diana to tea,' said Marilla. 'Here's a bottle of fruit juice. You can give some to Diana,' she said.

Anne was very excited about this. Tea time soon arrived and Anne and Diana were together. They had a wonderful time, having tea, and chatting like adults. Then Anne gave Diana some fruit juice. Diana drank not one, not two, but three glasses of fruit juice. Anne chatted a lot, as

---

[1] **to hope** when you want something to happen (or not happen)

Marilla goes out for the afternoon and Anne and Diana stay at home. Anne gives Diana what she thinks is some fruit juice but it's really medicine and after three glasses, Diana doesn't feel well.

usual. But soon Diana didn't feel very well. She had to go home.

Anne was very sad about this. 'Poor Diana,' she thought.

On the next day, Anne understood the problem. Marilla wanted to talk to Anne.

'Diana's mother is very angry. Diana returned home yesterday and she wasn't very well. What did you give Diana to drink?' asked Marilla.

'Only fruit juice,' said Anne.

Marilla looked in the kitchen. She saw a bottle. But it wasn't a bottle of fruit juice. It was a bottle of medicine[1]. A bottle of red medicine. The fruit juice was in a different place. ■

▶9   Marilla and Anne tried to explain[2] everything to Diana's mother, Mrs. Barry. Mrs. Barry was tall, with black hair, and black eyes, like Diana. ■

▶10   'It was a mistake[3]. We're sorry,' they both said.

But Mrs. Barry didn't forgive Anne. She didn't believe Anne. And she didn't want Diana to play with Anne anymore. *What can I do?* thought Anne.

---

[1] **medicine** something a doctor gives you to make you better
[2] **to explain** to tell someone something so that they can understand
[3] **mistake** an error, something you do wrong

The next afternoon, Diana came to say goodbye.

'Oh Diana, please think of me sometimes.'

'Of course,' replied Diana.

The following morning, Anne prepared[1] her school books.

'I'm going back to school. I can't speak to Diana, but I can see her.' ◉

Marilla and Anne apologise to Diana's mum about the medicine, but Mrs. Barry doesn't forgive them. Anne decides to go back to school because it's the only way she can see Diana.

Think

Why do you think Mrs. Barry doesn't forgive Marilla and Anne?

[1] **to prepare** to get ready

Reading

❶ Read the sentences and put the names of the people in the gaps.

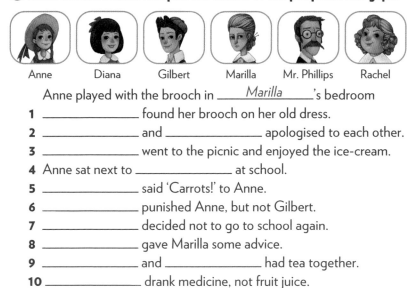

Anne   Diana   Gilbert   Marilla   Mr. Phillips   Rachel

Anne played with the brooch in _____*Marilla*_____'s bedroom

1 _____ found her brooch on her old dress.

2 _____ and _____ apologised to each other.

3 _____ went to the picnic and enjoyed the ice-cream.

4 Anne sat next to _____ at school.

5 _____ said 'Carrots!' to Anne.

6 _____ punished Anne, but not Gilbert.

7 _____ decided not to go to school again.

8 _____ gave Marilla some advice.

9 _____ and _____ had tea together.

10 _____ drank medicine, not fruit juice.

Vocabulary

❷ Complete this new dialogue between Anne and Mrs. Barry. Use the words in the box.

being	forgive	have	know	play	~~say~~	want

Anne 'Oh Mrs. Barry, I'd like to _____*say*_____ that I'm sorry. Please forgive me. I didn't **(1)** _____ to give Diana medicine.
I'm only a little orphan girl, and I only **(2)** _____ one friend in the world. That friend is Diana.
I didn't **(3)** _____ that it was medicine, and not fruit juice.
Please don't say that I can't **(4)** _____ with Diana anymore.
I enjoy **(5)** _____ with her so much.

Mrs. Barry 'I can't **(6)** _____ you. You mustn't play with my daughter again. Now go home and be a good girl.'

Reading and Writing MOVERS

3 **Look at this picture again. Complete the sentences and answer the questions.**

The people are in the   _classroom_ .

1 Where's the blackboard?   _____

2 Mr. Phillips is wearing a white   _____ .

3 How many books are there in the picture?   _____

4 What's Anne doing?   _____

Speaking and Writing

4 **Discuss these questions with a partner and write your answers.**

1 Anne loves the picnic. Where do you think the best place is to have a picnic?

    21st Century Skills

2 Anne says the food was delicious. What kind of things do you like eating on a picnic?

3 What's your favourite ice cream?

4 When do you eat in a restaurant?

5 Who cooks at home?

Before-reading Activity

Listening

▶ 11 **5** **Listen to the first part of Chapter 4 and complete these sentences with the right name.**

Diana wrote __Anne__ a letter.

1 Anne and _____ were always the best in the class at school.

2 Anne and _____ were alone at home that evening.

3 _____ came to Green Gables.

4 _____ is Minnie May's sister.

5 _____ wasn't well.

6 _____ went to find a doctor.

Chapter 4

Anne and her Adventure[1]

▶ 11 At school, Diana wrote a letter to Anne.

Dear Anne,

I can't play with you, but I'll always be your special friend. I'll always love you.

Your true friend,

Diana

Anne was sad, but she was happy to read the letter. Anne studied a lot at school. Soon, Anne and Gilbert were the best in the class. Sometimes Anne was the best and sometimes Gilbert was the best. Anne wanted to learn a lot of things.

One day, Marilla had to go out. 'I'll be back tomorrow,' said Marilla. 'So it's just you and Matthew at home tonight.'

Anne had lots of things to do. She studied for school. It was important to study hard. She wanted to be better than Gilbert. In the evening, Diana came to Green Gables. She was very worried.

[1] **adventure** something exciting and new that you do

'Come quickly! My baby sister, Minnie May, isn't well. Mother and father aren't at home. I don't know what to do.'

Matthew went out to find the doctor.

'Don't worry about your little sister,' said Anne. 'I know what to do.' ⬛

12   Anne went to Diana's house. She made some medicine. The two girls worked all night. They helped Minnie May to feel better. The house was warm and there was lots of hot water. At three o'clock in the morning, Matthew arrived with the doctor. Thanks to Anne, the baby was better. Anne went home. She was very tired.

'Thanks to Anne, the baby is better,' said the doctor to Diana's mother.

Anne slept for a long time. Then Marilla woke Anne up. She wanted to tell Anne something.

'Diana's mother was here this afternoon, Anne. She wanted to see you, but I didn't want to wake you up. You saved[1] Minnie May's life. She knows about the fruit juice. She knows it was a mistake. You and Diana can be best friends again.'

So Anne, and Diana, were friends again.

Diana asks Matthew and Anne to help her with her little sister, who isn't well. Anne stays with the baby while Matthew gets the doctor. Thanks to Anne, the baby gets better and Mrs. Barry says Anne and Diana can be friends again.

---

[1] **to save someone's life** to stop someone from dying

One evening, Anne was with Marilla at Green Gables.

'Oh Marilla, do you know that tomorrow is Diana's birthday,' said Anne. 'Can I go home with Diana, after school? Can I spend[1] the night at Diana's house? In the evening there's a concert[2]. Can I go?'

Marilla agreed. After school, Anne went to Diana's house. Then she went to the concert. Anne loved the concert. There was only one thing she didn't enjoy. She didn't like watching Gilbert read something. Anne didn't look at Gilbert. After the concert, the two girls went home. It was very late. They ran into their bedroom and got into bed, but something moved in the bed. Both Anne and Diana were frightened. It was Diana's Aunt Josephine. Diana didn't know that her aunt was in the bed. Now the two girls had to sleep in Minnie May's room.

'Aunt Josephine will be very angry about this. I didn't know that she was here, at my house, in that bedroom,' said Diana. 'She arrived this evening, when we were at the concert.'

On Diana's birthday, the girls go to a concert. Anne doesn't like it when Gilbert reads something. Then the girls go back to Diana's house to sleep but Diana's Aunt Josephine is in Diana's bed.

[1] **to spend (time)** to stay
[2] **concert** you can listen to people playing music, singing or reading something at a concert

Aunt Josephine was an old woman. She didn't like surprises, so she wasn't happy with Diana. Aunt Josephine wanted to go home immediately[1]. Now Diana was worried. Aunt Josephine was very rich. She paid for[2] Diana's music lessons. 'Maybe I can't have music lessons anymore,' thought Diana.

Anne tried to help Diana. She decided to apologise to Diana's Aunt Josephine. 'I'm sorry Miss Josephine. Don't be angry with Diana. It was me who got in the bed. Diana is a very good girl. Please can Diana have her music lessons? She loves music very, very much.'

Miss Josephine liked Anne.

'I'll forgive Diana. Anne, you must come and talk to me sometimes.'

Anne agreed.

That evening, Miss Josephine decided to stay. She gave Diana a present. 'I'd like to stay now. I want to see more of Anne. She's very interesting,' said Miss Josephine.

So Anne and Miss Josephine became friends.

One June evening, Marilla and Anne were at Green Gables. Marilla had a headache[3].

Anne helps Diana by apologising to her Aunt Josephine for jumping into the bed the night before. Diana can still do her music lessons that her aunt pays for.

---

[1] **immediately** now, at that moment
[2] **to pay for** to give money to buy something
[3] **headache** when your head hurts

'Marilla, do you remember? One year ago I arrived at Green Gables,' said Anne. 'Are you sorry that I stayed?'

'No,' said Marilla. Marilla couldn't live without Anne. But she didn't tell Anne this.

On the last day of June, it was the end of school. There were two months of holidays and there was another thing to be excited about. A new minister[1] and his wife came to Avonlea. They were Mr. and Mrs. Allen. One day, they came to Green Gables for tea. Anne made a cake. Anne waited for them to try it, but they ate so many things! They didn't want to eat it. Then Mrs. Allen saw Anne's face. Anne was so sad. So Mrs. Allen, and the others, ate some of Anne's cake.

'Anne, what did you put in this cake?' asked Marilla. 'It's strange!'

Anne ate some of the cake. Then she realised[2]. There was salt in the cake, and not sugar. It was horrible! Anne went to her room to cry.

Mrs Allen went to Anne's bedroom. 'My dear Anne,' she said. 'You mustn't cry. It was only a

[1] **minister** a man of the church
[2] **to realise** to understand

mistake. I like you, because you're kind[1]. It was kind of you to make the cake for us.'

Anne was happy again. Later, she said to Marilla, 'Isn't it nice to think that tomorrow is a new day with no mistakes. I know that I'll never make the same mistakes again.'

'But you always make new mistakes!' said Marilla.

Marilla was right. A month later, Anne made another big mistake. She was at Diana's house. There were lots of children in the garden. A girl said to Anne, 'Look at the house. The roof[2] is very high.'

Anne says she never makes the same mistake twice but Marilla says that Anne always makes new ones.

'It's not very high,' replied Anne.

'Walk on the top of the house then,' said the girl.

Anne walked to the house and said, 'OK, I'll do it!'

'No, Anne, don't do it. It's dangerous,' said Diana. But Anne wanted to do it. She went onto the roof. She walked slowly, and carefully. But,... then,... she fell!

The other children ran to her, 'Anne, are you dead?' asked Diana.

---

[1] **kind** a kind person is nice and wants to help other people
[2] **roof** the top of a house, see picture on page 47

Lucy Maud Montgomery

Anne makes another mistake. She walks on the roof of the house, but she falls and breaks her leg.

'No, but it's my leg. I think it's broken,' said Anne. She was right! Poor Anne had to stay at home for seven weeks! ◼

Think

Do you feel sorry for Anne? Why / Why not?

> Anne is walking on the roof of the house! It's very dangerous!

46

Reading

① **Read the sentences and underline the correct answer.**

Minnie May got better because *the doctor* / <u>*Anne*</u> helped her.

1 Anne slept for a long time because *she went to bed late /
her house was warm.*

2 Anne didn't enjoy *the concert / Gilbert's reading.*

3 Anne and Diana *knew / didn't know* that Aunt Josephine was
in the bedroom.

4 Aunt Josephine was angry with *Anne / Diana.*

5 *Anne / Diana* apologised to Aunt Josephine.

6 Anne's cake was *nice / horrible.*

7 Anne *didn't want to / wanted to* walk on the roof of the house.

Grammar

② **Complete each sentence with the correct preposition.**

| in | about | ~~at~~ | at | in | into | to | at | in |

Anne studied a lot __*at*__ school.

1 Diana came _____ Green Gables.

2 Diana's mother and father were not _____ home.

3 Anne spent the night _____ Diana's house.

4 Anne and Diana ran _____ the bedroom.

5 Something moved _____ the bed.

6 'Aunt Josephine will be very angry _____ this,' said Diana.

7 Anne put salt _____ her cake.

8 All the children were _____ the garden.

Speaking

③ **Answer the questions with a partner.
Do you agree about everything?**

21st
Century
Skills

1 Diana writes a letter to Anne. Do you ever write letters?
How do you speak to your friends when they aren't with you?

2 Anne studied a lot at school. How important do you think
it is to study hard at school?

Reading and Writing MOVERS

4 **Look at this picture again.**
Complete the sentences and answer the questions.

The ladder at the side of the house is _____black_____ .

1 Where's Anne? _____
2 Anne's hat is green and _____ .
3 How many steps can you see on the ladder? _____
4 What's Anne doing? _____

Before-reading Activities

Listening

(▶) 14 **5** **Listen to a part of Chapter 5. One statement is false.**
Which one is it? Tick true or false.

		T	F
	Marilla comes home late.	☑	☐
a	The dinner isn't ready.	☐	☐
b	Anne is sleeping.	☐	☐
c	Marilla is angry.	☐	☐
d	Anne gets up.	☐	☐

Speaking

6 **Anne wants Marilla to look at her hair. Look at page 53 to see why.**

3 Were you surprised that Anne knew how to help the baby? Why / Why not?
4 Anne spends the night with Diana. How often do you sleep over at a friend's house?
5 Anne goes to the concert. How often do you go to concerts? What kind of music do you like?

Chapter 5

More Adventures

▶ 13 One day, Matthew saw Anne with her classmates. There was something different about Anne. She was different from the other girls. Anne had a plain, dark dress. The other girls had red, and blue, and pink dresses. Matthew decided to buy a nice dress for Anne, but he couldn't go to the shop. He was too shy[1]. So, he asked Rachel for some advice.

Matthew sees the other girls all wearing nice dresses, so he wants one for Anne, too. Rachel helps by buying it. Anne gets it for Christmas with new shoes from Diana.

'I can buy the dress,' said Rachel. 'It must be a beautiful dress.'

Just before Christmas, Rachel brought the dress to Green Gables. Marilla didn't like it. She liked plain, dark dresses. This dress was a golden brown. On Christmas day, Matthew gave the dress to Anne.

'It's beautiful,' said Anne. She was very excited. Later, Diana arrived with another present for Anne - a pair of shoes.

'Diana, this is too much,' said Anne. 'I'm a very lucky girl.'

Everything was perfect[2]. Time passed, with no

[1] **shy** shy people find it hard to talk to people they don't know
[2] **perfect** everything is right

surprises. Soon, Anne was thirteen years old. And then, there was another surprise. ▣

▶14   One day, in spring, Marilla came home late. There was nothing ready for dinner. *What's Anne doing?* thought Marilla. *I asked her to make the dinner.* Marilla went into Anne's bedroom. Anne was in her bed.

'Are you sleeping?' asked Marilla.

'No,' said Anne.

'Aren't you well?'

'I'm well,' replied Anne.

'Get up then!' said Marilla. Marilla was angry. 'What's the problem?'

Anne got up. 'Look Marilla! Look at my hair!' ▣

▶15   'What?... Oh, no!' said Marilla. 'It's green!'

'Yes, I know, Marilla. I didn't want my hair to be green ... but a man came to Green Gables. I bought a bottle from him.'

'What are you talking about?' asked Marilla.

'I bought some medicine from this man. I put the medicine on my hair. I wanted to change the colour of my hair. I wanted my hair to be a beautiful dark colour, but it's not dark, it's horrible ... and it's green. I finished the bottle, but it's no good. Oh Marilla! What can I do?'

'Never buy things from strange men!' said Marilla.

Anne washed her hair, but it stayed green.

> Anne wants to change the colour of her hair so she buys some special medicine but her hair goes green - not the dark colour she wanted.

Anne stayed at home for a week. She washed her hair every day, but after a week, her hair was still green. 'Oh well,' said Anne. 'I can't go to school with green hair. It's better to have no hair at all.' So Anne went to school on Monday, with no hair. Some of the children laughed at her, but she didn't get angry. This was her punishment.

Anne was also worried about Marilla. 'I'm having bad headaches,' said Marilla to Anne. 'I must see a doctor.'

Anne also had time to play with her friends. One day, Anne and her friends played a game. They sat by the Lake of Shining Waters. A good imagination was very important for this game, so Anne used her imagination.

'I'm a princess and I'm dead. Put me in this boat. I'll cross the lake. Run to the other side of the lake. Wait for me there.'

Anne's friends put Anne into the boat. Then they ran.

At first, Anne enjoyed herself. It was romantic[1]. It was fun, but then she noticed[2] that something was wrong. 'Help, Help! My boat is sinking[3]!' cried Anne. But her friends couldn't hear her.

Anne is looking at herself in the mirror. Her hair is green!

[1] **romantic** to do with love
[2] **to notice** to see
[3] **to sink** when a boat sinks, it goes under the water

At that moment the boat went under a bridge[1]. It hit something. It was a post[2]. Anne put her hands on the post, and got out of the boat, but Anne's friends could only see the boat.

'Oh, no!' cried Diana. 'The boat is sinking, and Anne is in it.'

They didn't know that Anne wasn't in the boat. Anne was cold and wet, but she was safe. She didn't know what to do.

Then she saw Gilbert. He was in another boat. He saw Anne and said, 'Anne, what happened? Give me your hand.'

Anne got into Gilbert's boat. 'Thank you,' she said.

'Anne, look, can we be friends now? I'm sorry I said "carrots" to you. I want to be your friend,' said Gilbert.

Anne thought for a moment. *No, it's not possible*, thought Anne.

'No, I'm sorry, but we can't be friends,' she said.

'I'll never ask you to be my friend again,' said Gilbert. He was very angry.

Then Diana arrived. She was so happy to see Anne. 'I was so frightened,' said Diana.

> Anne uses a post to get out of the sinking boat. Then Gilbert helps her into his boat. He says he's sorry and asks Anne to be friends but she says no.

[1] **bridge** you walk on this to go from one side of a lake or river to the other. Look at the picture on page 55
[2] **post** Anne uses one of these to get out of her boat. Look at the picture on page 55

Gilbert sees Anne in the water and comes to help her with his boat.

'Me too,' replied Anne.

One day, Diana visited Anne at Green Gables. 'Anne, there's some good news. Aunt Josephine wants us to come to her house in town.'

'That's very exciting,' said Anne. 'There are lots of interesting things to do in town.'

The next Tuesday, the two girls went to town. They went to the park, and to a concert. They had a wonderful time. But after two days, Anne was happy to go home.

There's no place like Green Gables, she thought. Marilla was also happy to see Anne again. But she didn't tell Anne this. She gave Anne some important news. 'Anne, your teacher, Miss Stacey, visited me the other day. She wants to organise[1] a class for advanced[2] students. She wants to prepare this class to go to Queen's Academy. You're in the class!'

This was Anne's dream. At Queen's Academy you could learn to be a teacher, but Anne worried that it was expensive.

'Marilla, how can you pay for Queen's?' she asked.

'We have the money,' said Marilla. 'And we want you to have a good education[3].'

Anne and Diana go to town to visit Diana's aunt. Anne likes the town but she thinks Green Gables is the best place to be.

Anne is in the advanced class to study to go to Queen's Academy where she can learn to be a teacher. This is her dream.

---

[1] **organise** when you do everything to make something go well
[2] **advanced** (here) the best
[3] **education** what you learn at school

Anne had to stay at school for an extra[1] hour every day. She had to pass[2] an exam[3] to go to Queen's. There were seven students in the advanced class. Gilbert was in the class but Diana wasn't. *I want to go to Queen's*, thought Anne. *Then Marilla and Matthew will be so proud of me[4].*

The advanced course began. Time passed quickly. Summer arrived, then autumn, then winter, and then spring. Anne studied a lot at school. She had no time for mistakes, or surprises. Soon Anne was fifteen years old. She thought about the exam. *I must pass the exam,* thought Anne. *I must pass the exam for Marilla and Matthew! Then I can go to Queen's.*

At the end of June, Anne's lessons finished. Anne and Diana walked home from school.

'It's the end of everything,' said Diana. 'You'll pass the exam, and then you won't go to school here again. It'll be very sad without you.'

'Don't worry, I won't pass,' replied Anne.

But Anne wanted to pass. She wanted to see Matthew's happy face. (■)

Anne studies hard to go to Queen's because she wants to make Matthew and Marilla happy. She's only sad that Diana can't come with her.

---

[1] **extra (hour)** one **(hour)** more
[2] **pass (an exam)** do well
[3] **exam** in an exam there are questions to see how much you know
[4] **to be proud of** to be pleased about something that somebody you love does

Reading

1 Look at the sentences. Decide who's speaking.

> Anne   Diana   Gilbert   Marilla
> ~~Matthew~~   Miss Stacey   Rachel

'Anne's dresses are very plain and dark.' ___Matthew___

1 'I can buy a dress for Anne.' _____
2 'I hope that Anne likes the shoes.' _____
3 'Anne, you mustn't buy things from strange men.' _____
4 'I'm cold and wet. Who's going to save me?' _____
5 'I'd like to be friends with Anne.' _____
6 'I'm the teacher of an advanced course this year.' _____

Reading and Writing **MOVERS**

2 Choose the correct word for each sentence.

___On___ Christmas Day, Diana brought Anne new shoes.

> ~~On~~   At   In

1 Marilla was _____ because there was nothing ready for dinner.

> happy   angry   excited

2 Anne wanted her hair _____ a beautiful dark colour, not green.

> be   being   to be

3 Marilla _____ see a doctor about her bad headaches.

> can   must   wants

4 Diana was very _____ because she couldn't see Anne in the sinking boat.

> excited   angry   frightened

5 Diana _____ go to Queen's Academy because she isn't in the advanced class.

> mustn't   can't   don't

58

Grammar

③ Put the words in the correct order to make questions.

sleeping are you? A_re you sleeping?_

1 well you aren't? A_____

2 problem what's the? W_____

3 do I what can? W_____

4 be we can friends? C_____

5 for Queen's pay you how can? H_____

Speaking

21st Century Skills

④ Talk to a partner about these questions and answer them. Are any of your answers the same?

1 Anne doesn't like the colour of her hair. Is there anything you'd like to change about yourself?

2 What do you think is more important, what a person looks like or what they are like inside?

3 Gilbert saves Anne and says he's sorry for calling her 'carrots' but Anne doesn't want to be friends with him. Do you think she's right? Why / Why not?

4 When do you get angry with your friends or classmates?

Before-reading Activity

Listening

▶ 16 **⑤ Listen to the first part of Chapter 6 and choose A, B, or C.**

Anne waited for the exam results for

A ☐ one week. **B** ☐ two weeks. **C** ☑ three weeks.

1 Who told Anne about the results?

A ☐ Diana **B** ☐ Gilbert **C** ☐ Matthew

2 Who was in first place?

A ☐ Gilbert **B** ☐ Both Anne and Gilbert **C** ☐ Anne

3 When Anne talks to Matthew about the results,

A ☐ he smiles. **B** ☐ he cries. **C** ☐ he laughs.

4 When Anne talks to Marilla about the results,

A ☐ she smiles. **B** ☐ she cries. **C** ☐ she laughs.

Chapter 6

Endings and Beginnings

16 Anne waited for the exam results[1]. One week passed! Two weeks passed! Then, after three weeks, Diana arrived at Green Gables. She had some news. 'Look at the results. You did really well. You and Gilbert are in first place! You're going to Queen's!'

Anne comes first in the exam with Gilbert and in September she starts studying at Queen's.

Anne ran outside to tell Matthew. 'Matthew, look at the list[2]! First place!' Matthew looked at the list. There was a smile on his face.

Marilla didn't smile. She cried. 'You're going away now. What will I do without you?' ■

17 'Don't worry, Marilla,' said Anne. 'I'll always be your little girl. I'll always love you, and Matthew, and Green Gables.'

In September, the day finally arrived. Anne went to Queen's. On the first day, she met all the students and teachers. There were fifty other students. Every spring, at Queen's, there were two prizes[3] for the best students. The winners[4] of

❯

Matthew is reading the results of Anne's exam and he's smiling because she's first on the list.

[1] **results** these tell you how well you did in an exam
[2] **list** when you write names of people or things one below the other
[3] **prize** something special that you get if you're the best
[4] **winner** the person who's the best

the prizes went to Redmond College. This was a very important college.

Anne worked hard at Queen's in the winter months. She enjoyed her time there, but she went home every weekend. Sometimes, Anne thought of Gilbert. *I want to have a friend like Gilbert,* she thought. *I want to talk to him about lots of things.*

Anne did well at Queen's, and soon spring arrived.

I love spring, thought Anne. *But spring this year is different. Now the Academy must choose the top two students. I want to go to Redmond College.*

The day arrived. *Who are the top two students? Who will win the prizes?* thought Anne.

Anne arrived at Queen's and then she received[1] the news. The winners of the prizes were Gilbert Blythe... and Anne Shirley!

Anne! That's me, thought Anne. *Now I can go to Redmond College next September. I must write to Marilla and Matthew.*

Marilla and Matthew were very proud of their

---

[1] **receive** get

Anne. They came to visit Anne. And then Anne went home to Green Gables with them.

Some days passed, and then Diana arrived with some surprising news.

'Anne, Gilbert isn't going to Redmond College. He wants to be a teacher at our school in Avonlea.'

Anne didn't know why, but she was quite sad. *It'll be strange without Gilbert*, she thought.

At breakfast the next morning, Anne looked at Matthew. He wasn't well. 'He's having problems with his heart[1],' explained Marilla.

Anne looked at Marilla. 'You're also not well, Marilla. You work too hard. You must rest[2] now that I'm at home.'

'Well, a special doctor is coming here in June. I must see him.'

Then Marilla told Anne some more bad news. 'All our money is in the bank, and the bank is having problems. I'm worried about our money.'

Later that day, Anne talked to Matthew. 'You work too hard,' said Anne. 'I'd like to help you, but you need a boy.'

'I prefer[3] you to one hundred boys,' said

Gilbert wants to be a teacher at Avonlea. Anne is sad that he doesn't want to go to college with her. Anne is also worried about Matthew and Marilla. Matthew has a bad heart and Marilla works too hard. They're also worried about the bank where all their money is because the bank has problems.

[1] **heart**
[2] **to rest** not to work
[3] **to prefer** to like better

Matthew. 'My girl, who I'm proud of.'

Anne always remembered that moment. It was her last conversation with her dear Matthew.

The next morning, Matthew came out of the house and something terrible happened. Matthew fell down.

'Matthew! Matthew! Are you alright?' cried Marilla. 'Anne, we must get the doctor!'

Anne and Marilla tried to help Matthew.

'Oh, Marilla,' said Anne, 'I don't think we can help him anymore.'

'You're right,' said Marilla.

The doctor arrived. He told Anne and Marilla the terrible news.

'Matthew is dead. He probably died from a shock[1].'

Anne and Marilla looked at a piece of paper in Matthew's hand. That was the shock. It was a letter from the bank. Their bank didn't have any more money.

This also means that we don't have any money, thought Marilla.

Anne was very sad. She didn't want to speak

Matthew dies after reading a letter from the bank. The bank doesn't have any more money, so Marilla has no money now.

Anne is crying because Matthew is dead. Marilla hears her and comes to her bedroom.

¹ **shock** a terrible surprise

to other people. In her bedroom, Anne tried to cry, but she couldn't cry. Then she remembered Matthew's last words:

'My girl, who I'm proud of.'

Marilla tells Anne she loves her for the first time. Now they only have each other.

Then Anne cried. Marilla heard Anne. She went into her bedroom. They sat together.

'Oh, Marilla, what can we do without Matthew?' said Anne.

'I have you, Anne and you have me.'

Then Marilla said something to Anne for the first time.

'Anne, you know that I love you very much.' Anne and Marilla sat together, and thought of Matthew.

Two days later, the minister's wife, Mrs. Allen, visited Anne. 'Remember to be happy... for Matthew, and for Marilla,' said Mrs. Allen. 'Matthew liked to see your happy face. Marilla will be very sad when you go away to Redmond College.'

Anne didn't say anything.

It was difficult to think of life without Matthew.

But Marilla had to see the doctor.

When Marilla returned Anne asked her, 'What did the doctor say?'

'He said that I must wear glasses, and I must stop reading. Oh Anne, what if I go blind[1]? What can I do?'

'Don't worry,' said Anne, 'the glasses will stop your headaches and I'm sure you aren't going blind.'

'There's another thing I have to say,' said Marilla. 'I am selling[2] Green Gables.'

'Oh, Marilla, don't sell Green Gables!' said Anne.

'What can I do? We don't have any money,' said Marilla.

'You mustn't sell Green Gables. You don't have to stay here alone. I'm staying with you. I'm not going to Redmond College. I can teach now. I can teach at a school near here. In the summer, I can come back home every day and in the winter, I can come home at weekends.'

'Oh, Anne, I know I can be happy with you here. But what about your plans[3]?'

'I have a plan,' said Anne. 'And that is to be a

Marilla sees the doctor and she must wear glasses. She's worried about going blind. Then she says she must sell Green Gables because they have no money.

---

[1] **to go blind** to not be able to see any more
[2] **sell** when you give something to someone for money
[3] **plan** an idea about what to do in the future

teacher. I don't want to lose Green Gables!'

Rachel heard the news. She came to Green Gables to speak to Anne. 'I think you're a very good girl to stay with Marilla,' said Rachel. 'You can teach here in Avonlea.'

'But what about Gilbert?' asked Anne.

'Gilbert knows that you're staying at Green Gables, so, he decided not to teach in Avonlea. He wants you to teach in Avonlea. He's going to another school.'

Anne was so happy. She could come home every day to Green Gables! She could be with Marilla every day.

The next evening, Anne went for a walk. She saw a boy near her. It was Gilbert! Anne stopped him and said, 'Gilbert thank you for giving Avonlea school to me. It was very kind of you.'

'I was happy to help you,' said Gilbert. 'Now, can we be friends?'

Anne laughed. 'We can be the best of friends.'

And so Anne and Gilbert walked home.

I want to be happy now, for Matthew, thought

Anne. *I have my imagination. I have a new friend and I can be a teacher. What an exciting future!* ◉

Anne says thank you to Gilbert for Avonlea School. Now they're friends and Anne is happy about everything.

Think

What do you think of Gilbert?

Reading

1 Choose the correct option.

Matthew dies
a ☐ because he falls down.   b ☑ because of some bad news.

1 Marilla must
a ☐ wear glasses.   b ☐ buy glasses for Anne.

2 Anne doesn't go to
a ☐ Redmond College.   b ☐ Queen's.

3 Anne decides to stay at Green Gables
a ☐ to be near Marilla.   b ☐ to be near Diana.

4 Rachel visits Green Gables
a ☐ to speak to Anne.   b ☐ to speak to Marilla.

5 Gilbert doesn't teach at Avonlea
a ☐ so that Anne can   b ☐ so that he can go to
teach there.   Redmond College.

6 Anne and Gilbert
a ☐ don't want to be friends.   b ☐ want to be friends.

Reading and Writing   MOVERS

2 Look at this picture again. Complete the sentences and answer the questions.

The people are   ___outside___ .

1 Where are the trees?   _____

2 Matthew is wearing black   _____ .

3 Is Anne happy or sad?   _____

4 What's Matthew doing?   _____

Speaking and Writing

3 **Work with a partner and answer the questions.**
Do you agree on everything?

1 What did you like about the story?
2 What didn't you like?
3 What was the best part of the story?
4 Which person did you like best? Why?
5 Think of words to describe the people below and write them under each photo.

Vocabulary

4 **Put the words in the box into the correct category.**
Use the table below.

> bedroom   black   blackboard   breakfast   cake   classroom
> classmates   dress   exam   flowers   fruit juice   green   hat
> lake   kitchen   pink   pond   red   shoes   sweets

School	*blackboard*
Food and Drink	
Colours	
House	
Nature	
Clothes	

5 **Now add 2 more words you know to each category.**

Lucy Maud Montgomery

1874

Lucy Maud Montgomery
Born in 1874 on Prince Edward Island, Canada.
Lucy and Anne – from 2 years old, after her mother's death, she lived with her grandparents on their farm in Cavendish, on Prince Edward Island in Canada. Therefore, she was like Anne in the story of Green Gables. A lonely child, with a great imagination, Lucy loved reading and writing stories. At the age of 14, she started writing about her adventures in a diary.

1890

1893

Education and first job
In 1893, she went to college to study to be a teacher. She taught for three years and when her grandfather died in 1898, she stayed with her grandmother and wrote poems and stories.

Early life
Lucy's father married again in 1890 and she went to stay with him and his new wife, but she didn't like living there. At this time, Lucy wrote a poem for the newspaper, The Daily Patriot. In August 1891, she went back to her grandparents' farm.

1920

Later life
Lucy's grandmother died in 1911 and four months later, Lucy married Ewan MacDonald, a minister, and they had two sons.

Other works
In the early 1920s, she wrote another popular book, *Emily of New Moon*. In the 1930s, she wrote books for children, which were also very popular.

1930

Other stories about Anne
Lucy wrote eight books about Anne: *Anne of Green Gables*, *Anne of Avonlea*, *Anne of the Island*, *Anne of Windy Poplars*, *Anne's House of Dreams*, *Anne of Ingleside*, *Rainbow Valley* and *Rilla of Ingleside*.

Remembered for:
although she wrote over 20 books and hundreds of short stories and poems, she is best remembered for *Anne of Green Gables*, which many people still read today.

Anne of
GREEN
GABLES

L. M. MONTGOMERY

1942

Died
April 1942 in her home in Toronto.

1908

Anne of Green Gables
Lucy's first novel, it was a big success and one of her fans was the famous writer, Mark Twain. He described Anne as a dear and loveable character.

Arts and Entertainment

Anne of Green Gables is a very famous story. People from all over the world know and love it. You can find the book in thirty-six different languages. There are also films, plays, musicals, TV programmes and cartoons that tell the story of *Anne of Green Gables*. Here are some examples.

Avonlea

Fans of *Anne of Green Gables* can visit a very special place - Avonlea. Tourists go to Prince Edward Island to visit Avonlea, the village of Green Gables. The people who work at the village wear traditional costumes of the time. You can imagine what it was like to live in this small town in the 1880s. In the village there are many things to do. There are beautiful gardens. You can travel in a buggy, like Matthew, Marilla and Anne. It's also possible to visit a school similar to the one in the story. You can also eat ice-cream from the shop 'The Picnic Basket'.

**Look at these activities.
Tick (✓) the ones you have
to go to Canada to enjoy.**

☑ Travelling in a buggy, like Anne

1 ☐ Watching the film version

2 ☐ Watching the cartoon version

3 ☐ Eating ice-cream at the Picnic Basket

4 ☐ Watching the musical version

Films

There are three famous films of Anne of Green Gables. The first one is from 1919. It's a silent movie. There's no talking, and only music in the film. There's also a film made in 1934. The film was very popular. The actress, Dawn O'Day, was Anne in the film. She loved the character of Anne. And she changed her name to Anne after the film. The most famous version of the film is from 1985. The story of this film is very similar to the original story. The director, Kevin Sullivan, made the film in Canada.

Cartoons

There are also a lot of cartoon versions of Anne of Green Gables. The Japanese version, made in 1979, is very popular. This cartoon has fifty episodes. Later, the director of the cartoon used the first six episodes to make a film. The cartoon is very popular, especially in Italy and Germany.

The Natural Beauty of Canada

Anne loved nature. Canada is famous for its natural beauty. There are lots of lakes, national parks and mountains. Tourists come from all over the world to visit, every year. A lot of people come to enjoy activities on the lakes and in the mountains. Here are some examples of Canada's natural beauty.

1 The Canadian Rockies

The mountains of the Canadian Rockies are very beautiful. The government tries to protect this area. So, it remains clean and natural. There are five national parks. There are also lots of lakes in the area. You can also find interesting animals, like the famous grizzly bear. People who go to the Rockies have to be careful about the weather. The weather can change very quickly. On one side of the mountain, there can be rain. At the same time, on the other side, it can be sunny.

2 Niagara Falls

Niagara Falls is a famous tourist attraction. One part of Niagara Falls is in Canada and another part is in the United States. There are three waterfalls at Niagara Falls. The Canadian waterfall is called 'Horseshoe Falls'. The waterfall comes from the Niagara River. It's incredible to see because there's so much water. The water goes down very quickly because it falls from over 50 metres! There are boats that take people very near to the waterfall, then you can see how powerful it is.

3 Cabot Trail

The trail is in Nova Scotia. It has an interesting name. John Cabot was an Italian explorer who arrived in the area in 1497. The trail is three hundred kilometres long. There are beautiful views of the sea. Tourists go there with their cars to follow the trail. They can stop in a lot of different places to look at the sea. There are a lot of festivals in this area.

4 Baffin Island

Baffin Island is a very large island. There are a lot of beautiful places on the island. Not many people live there. It can be very cold. For two months in the summer, there's no night and for two months in the winter, there's no daylight.

Look at this list of things that you need to go to these places. Where do you think they are useful?

coat ___1 & 4___
a camera _____
b mobile phone _____
c raincoat _____
d swimming
   costume _____
e umbrella _____
f walking boots _____

Choose the correct answer, A, B, or C for each question.

Why is Matthew surprised to see Anne at the station?
- **a** ☐ Because she has red hair.
- **b** ☑ Because she's a girl.
- **c** ☐ Because she's early.

1 Anne didn't like her
- **a** ☐ hair.
- **b** ☐ eyes.
- **c** ☐ nose.

2 Anne's parents died when she was
- **a** ☐ three years old.
- **b** ☐ three weeks old.
- **c** ☐ three months old.

3 What does Marilla lose?
- **a** ☐ Her bracelet
- **b** ☐ Her brooch
- **c** ☐ Her ring

4 When Diana had tea with Anne, Diana drank
- **a** ☐ fruit juice.
- **b** ☐ medicine.
- **c** ☐ milk.

5 Anne broke her leg
- **a** ☐ at Green Gables.
- **b** ☐ at the Lake of Shining Waters.
- **c** ☐ at Diana's house.

6 What does Anne put in the cake that she makes for Mrs. Allen?
- **a** ☐ Salt
- **b** ☐ Sugar
- **c** ☐ Medicine

7 At the end of the story, Anne can teach
- **a** ☐ at a school near Avonlea.
- **b** ☐ at the school in Avonlea.
- **c** ☐ at Queen's College.

Syllabus

Topics
Home
School
Family
Nature
Colours
Clothing

Grammar and Structures
Simple Present: states and habits
Present Continuous: actions in progress
Past Simple: finished actions
Future with *will*
Can: ability
Could: ability
Must: obligation
Have to: necessity
Comparative and Superlative Adjectives
Adverbs
Prepositions (place, time)
Pronouns
Question words
Relative clauses
There is/There are
Verbs + infinitive/ing
When clauses

Teen ELi Readers

Stage 1
Maureen Simpson, *In Search of a Missing Friend*
Charles Dickens, *Oliver Twist*
Geoffrey Chaucer, *The Canterbury Tales*
Janet Borsbey & Ruth Swan, *The Boat Race Mystery*
Lucy Maud Montgomery, *Anne of Green Gables*
Mark Twain, *A Connecticut Yankee in King Arthur's Court*
Mark Twain, *The Adventures of Huckleberry Finn*
Angela Tomkinson, *Great Friends!*
Edith Nesbit, *The Railway Children*
Eleanor H. Porter, *Pollyanna*
Anna Sewell, *Black Beauty*
Kenneth Grahame, *The Wind in the Willows*

Stage 2
Elizabeth Ferretti, *Dear Diary...*
Angela Tomkinson, *Loving London*
Mark Twain, *The Adventures of Tom Sawyer*
Mary Flagan, *The Egyptian Souvenir*
Maria Luisa Banfi, *A Faraway World*
Frances Hodgson Burnett, *The Secret Garden*
Robert Louis Stevenson, *Treasure Island*
Elizabeth Ferretti, *Adventure at Haydon Point*
William Shakespeare, *The Tempest*
Angela Tomkinson, *Enjoy New York*
Frances Hodgson Burnett, *Little Lord Fauntleroy*
Michael Lacey Freeman, *Egghead*
Michael Lacey Freeman, *Dot to Dot*
Silvana Sardi, *The Boy with the Red Balloon*
Silvana Sardi, *Scotland is Magic!*
Silvana Sardi, *Garpur: My Iceland*
Silvana Sardi, *Follow your Dreams*
Gabriele Rebagliati, *Naoko: My Japan*

Stage 3
Anna Claudia Ramos, *Expedition Brazil*
Charles Dickens, *David Copperfield*
Mary Flagan, *Val's Diary*
Maureen Simpson, *Destination Karminia*
Anonymous, *Robin Hood*
Jack London, *The Call of the Wild*
Louisa May Alcott, *Little Women*
Gordon Gamlin, *Allan: My Vancouver*